Celine Dion

Wise Publications
London/New York/Paris/Sydney/
Copenhagen/Madrid

Exclusive Distributors:
Music Sales Limited
8/9 Frith Street, London W1V 5TZ, England.
Music Sales Pty Limited
120 Rothschild Avenue, Rosebery, NSW 2018, Australia.

Order No. AM957870
ISBN 0-7119-7377-6
This book © Copyright 1999 by Wise Publications

Compiled by Peter Evans
Music arranged by Stephen Duro
Music processed by Allegro Reproductions
Cover photograph courtesy Retna

Printed in the United Kingdom by
Halstan & Co Limited, Amersham, Buckinghamshire.

Your Guarantee of Quality
As publishers, we strive to produce every book to the highest commercial standards.
The music has been freshly engraved and the book has been carefully designed to minimise
awkward page turns and to make playing from it a real pleasure.

Particular care has been given to specifying acid-free, neutral-sized paper made from pulps
which have not been elemental chlorine bleached. This pulp is from farmed sustainable forests
and was produced with special regard for the environment.

Throughout, the printing and binding have been planned to ensure a sturdy, attractive publication
which should give years of enjoyment.

If your copy fails to meet our high standards, please inform us and we will gladly replace it.

Music Sales' complete catalogue describes thousands of titles and is available in full colour sections
by subject, direct from Music Sales Limited. Please state your areas of interest
and send a cheque/postal order for £1.50 for postage to:
Music Sales Limited, Newmarket Road, Bury St. Edmunds, Suffolk IP33 3YB.

www.musicinprint.com

My Heart Will Go On
(Love Theme from 'Titanic')

Words & Music by James Horner & Will Jennings

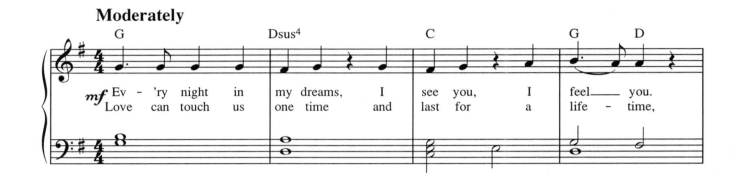

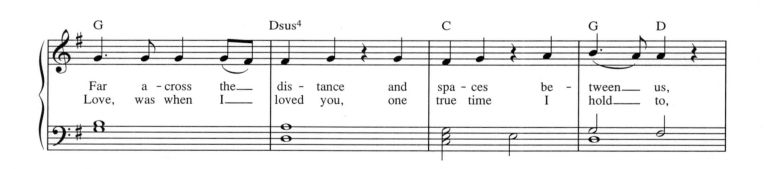

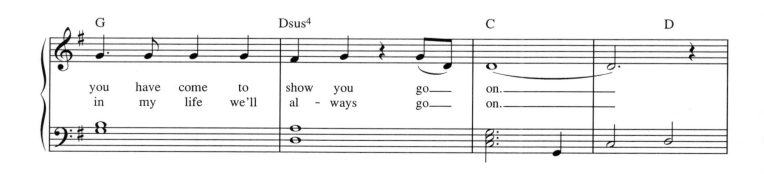

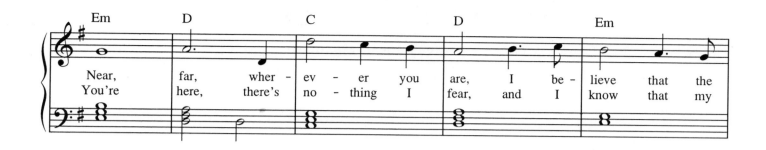

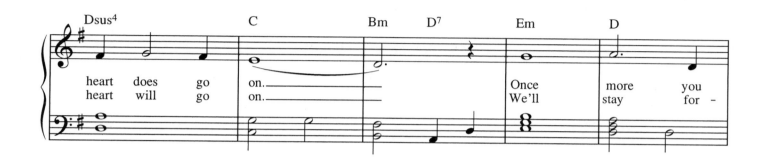

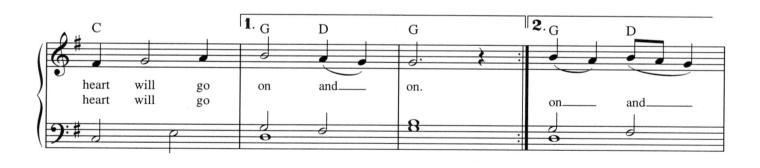

All By Myself

Words by Eric Carmen
Music by Sergei Rachmaninoff & Eric Carmen

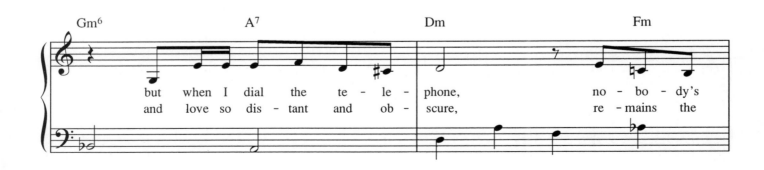

When I Need You

Words & Music by Albert Hammond & Carole Bayer Sager

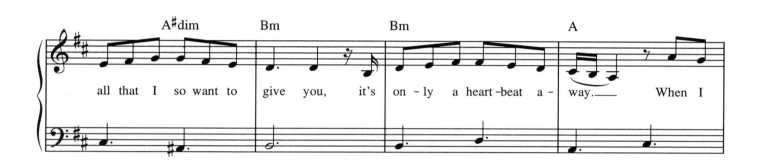

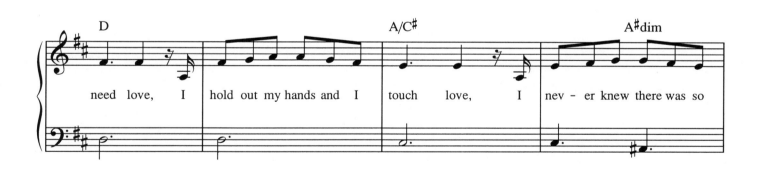

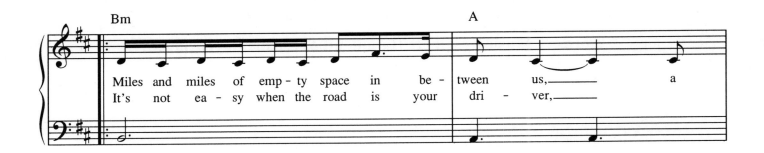

Miles and miles of emp-ty space in be - tween us,_____ a
It's not ea - sy when the road is your dri - ver,_____

te - le-phone can't take the place of your smile,_____ oh, but you know I won't be tra-vel-ling for
ho - ney that's a hea - vy load that we bear,_____ oh, but you know I won't be tra-vel-ling a

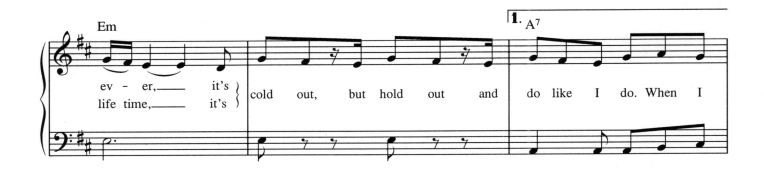

ev - er,_____ it's } cold out, but hold out and do like I do. When I
life time,_____ it's }

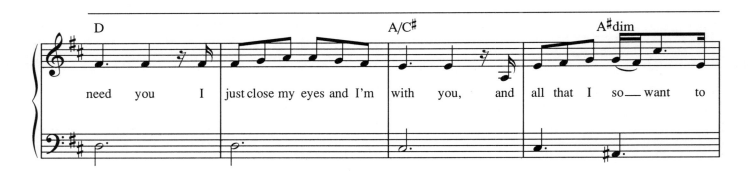

need you I just close my eyes and I'm with you, and all that I so___ want to

give you ba- by, it's on-ly a heart-beat a - way. do like I do._____

When I need love, I hold out my hands and I touch love,— and I nev-er knew, oh nev-er knew there was so much love,— keep-ing me warm night and day.— When I need you I just close my eyes and I'm with you, and all that I so want to give you, it's on-ly a heart beat a - way. When I -way. *ritardando*

1. A

2. A

Falling Into You

Words & Music by Rick Knowles,
Marie Claire D'Ubalio & Billy Steinberg

Moderately

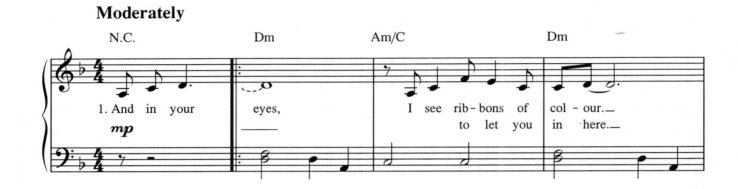

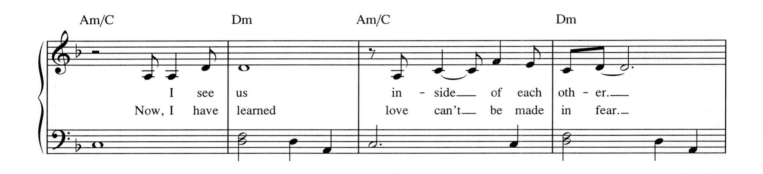

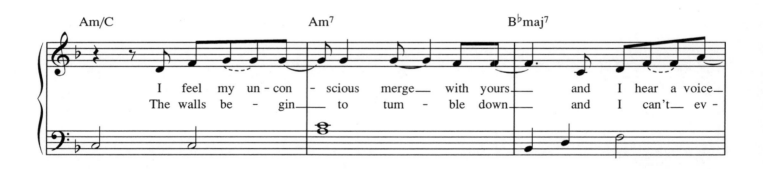

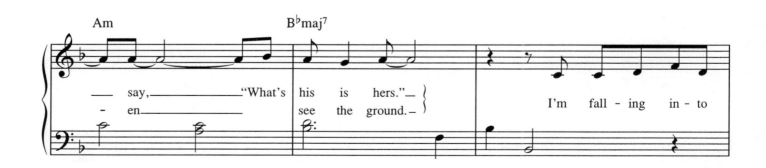

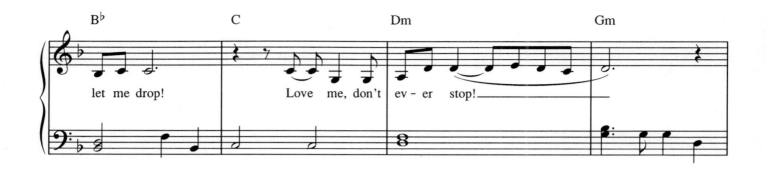

let me drop! Love me, don't ev - er stop!

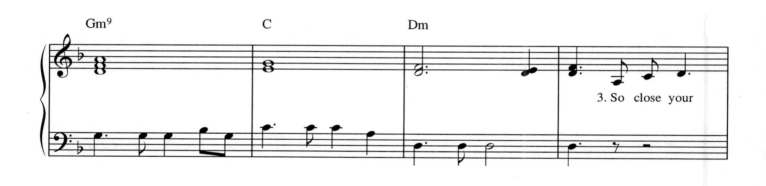

3. So close your

eyes   and let___ me   kiss you.___   And while

you sleep   I will   miss you.   Oh, I'm fall - ing in - to

CODA

you are.

Fall - ing in - to you,   fall - ing in - to you.

fall - ing in - to   you.

15

Immortality

Words & Music by Barry Gibb, Robin Gibb & Maurice Gibb

Moderately

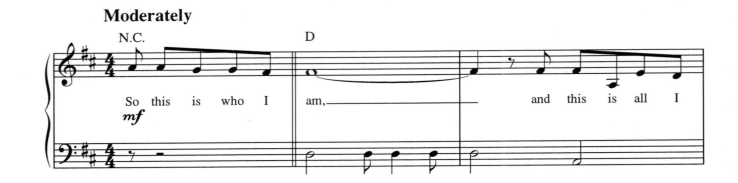

So this is who I am, and this is all I

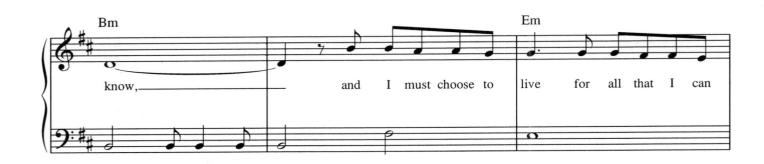

know, and I must choose to live for all that I can

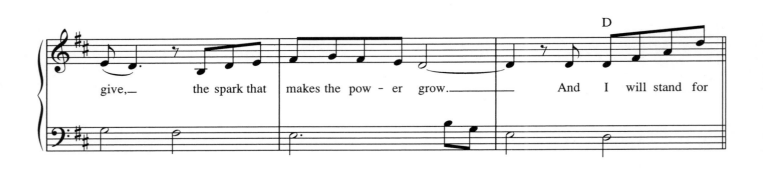

give, the spark that makes the pow - er grow. And I will stand for

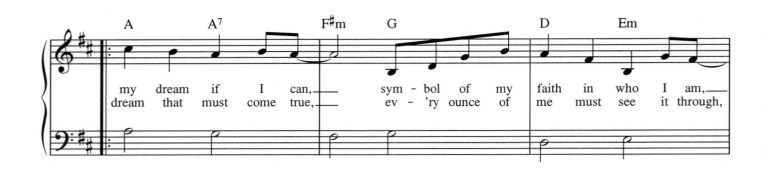

my dream if I can, sym - bol of my faith in who I am,
dream that must come true, ev - 'ry ounce of me must see it through,

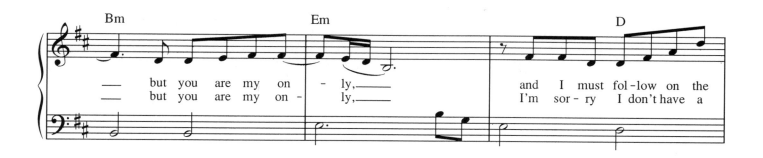

but you are my on - ly,___ and I must fol-low on the
but you are my on - ly,___ I'm sor - ry I don't have a

road that lies a - head,___ and I won't let my heart con-trol my head,___ but you are my on-
role for love to play,___ hand ov - er my heart, I'll find my way,___ I will make them

First time only

- ly,___ And we don't say,___ good-bye, we don't say good-
give to___ me.)

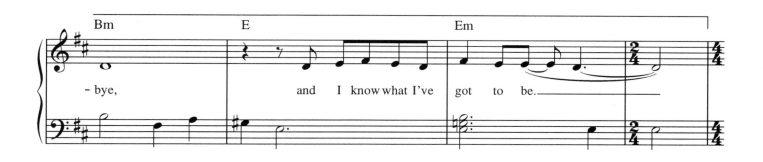

- bye, and I know what I've got to be.___

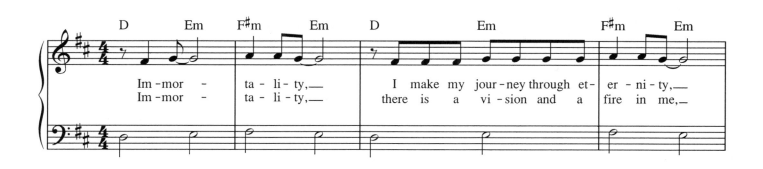

Im -mor - ta - li - ty,___ I make my jour-ney through et- er - ni - ty,___
Im -mor - ta - li - ty,___ there is a vi - sion and a fire in me,___

I keep the me-mo-ry of you and me,— in - side.——
I keep the me-mo-ry of you and me,— in - side.——

Ful-fill your des- ti -

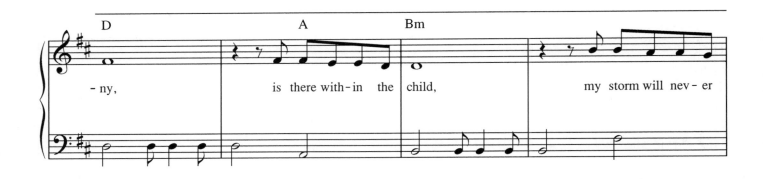

- ny, is there with-in the child, my storm will nev - er

end, my fate is on the wind,— the King of Hearts,— the jok - er's wild.

But we don't say— good-bye, we don't say good - bye.

I'll make them all re - mem - ber me._____ 'Cause I have found a

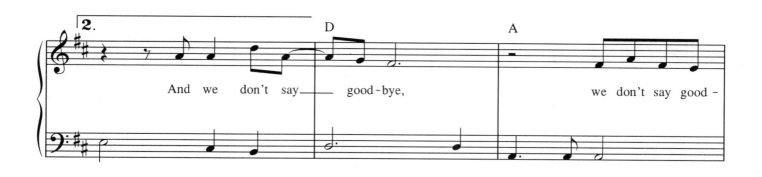

And we don't say____ good-bye, we don't say good -

- bye. with all my love for you,____ and what else we may

do. We don't say good - bye._____

Let's Talk About Love

Words & Music by Bryan Adams, Elliott Kennedy & Jean-Jacques Goldman

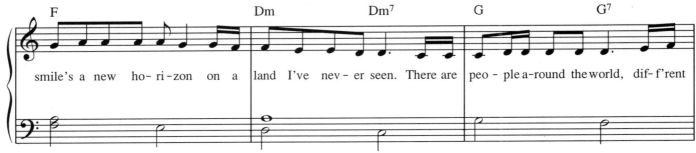

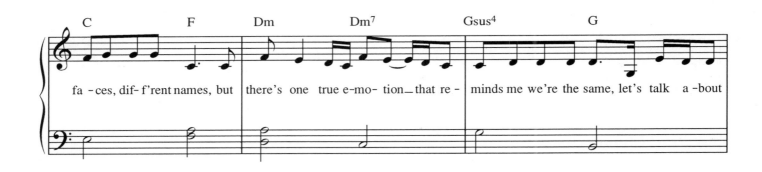

F   **Dm**   **Gm**

love,   let's talk a-bout___ us,   let's talk a-bout life,   let's talk a-bout___

C   **D**

trust.   *cresc.*

G   **Em**   **C**   **G**

Ev-'ry-where I go,   all the pla-ces that I've been,___ ev-'ry smile's a new ho-ri-zon, on a

Am   **Dsus⁴**   **D⁷**   **G**   **C**

land I've nev-er seen. There are peo-ple a-round the world, dif-f'rent fa-ces, dif-f'rent names, but

Am   **Dsus⁴**   **D**

there's one true e-mo-tion, that re-minds me we're the same.___ Let's talk a-bout___

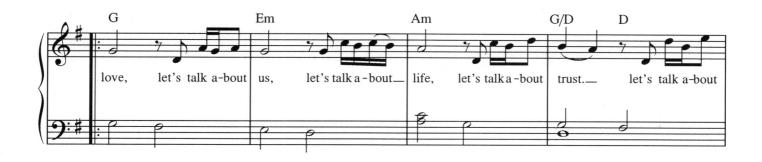

love,   let's talk a-bout us,   let's talk a-bout life,   let's talk a-bout trust.   let's talk a-bout

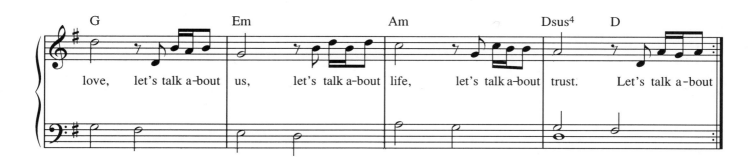

love,   let's talk a-bout us,   let's talk a-bout life,   let's talk a-bout trust.   Let's talk a-bout

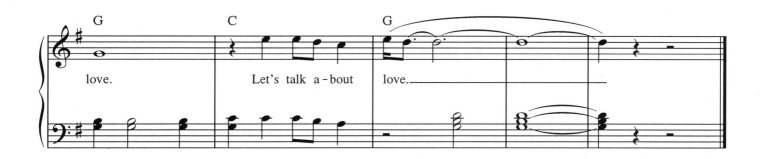

love.   Let's talk a-bout love._____

Verse 2:

From the laughter of a child
To the tears of a grown man
There's a threat that runs right through us
And helps us to understand.
As subtle as a breeze
That fans a flicker to a flame
From the very first sweet melody
To the very last refrain.

Love Doesn't Ask Why

Words & Music by Philip Galdston, Barry Mann & Cynthia Weil

Love does-n't ask why, it speaks from the heart and nev-er ex-plains. Don't you know that love does-n't think twice, it can come all at once

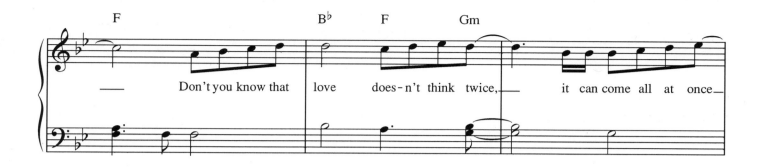

Don't you know that love does-n't think twice, — it can come all at once —

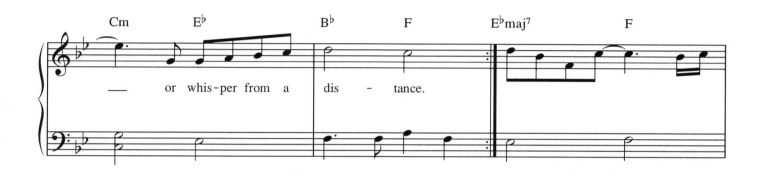

— or whis-per from a dis - tance.

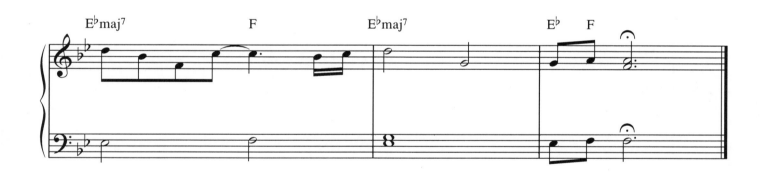

Verse 2:

Now I can feel what you're afraid to say.
If you give your soul to me,
Will you give too much away,
But we can't let this moment pass us by.
Can't question this chance
Or expect any answers.
We can try,
Maybe we can try.

Tell Him

Words & Music by Linda Thompson, Walter Afanasieff & David Foster

Moderately

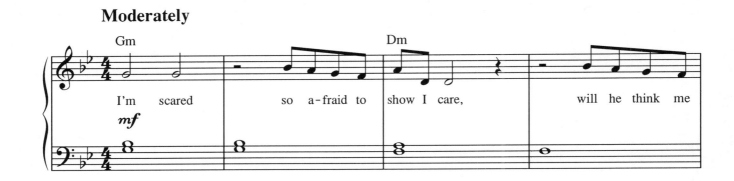

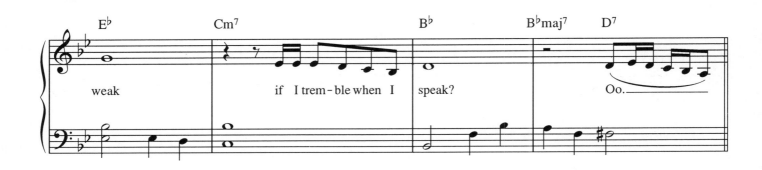

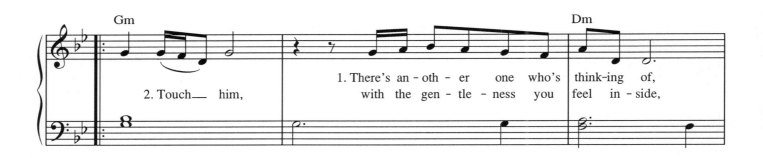

tell him that the sun and moon rise in his eyes, reach out to him____ and

whis - per, whis - per words so soft and sweet,____ hold him close to feel his heart-beat,

love will be the gift you give your- self,____ oo,____

ne - ver let him go.____

The Colour Of My Love

Words & Music by David Foster & Arthur Janov

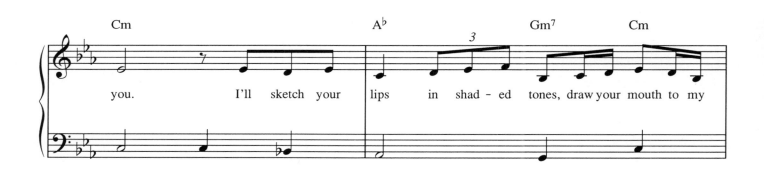

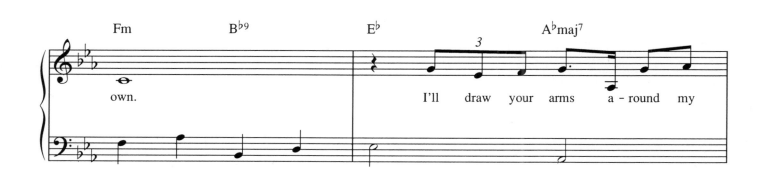

33

The Power Of Love

Words & Music by C. deRouge, G. Mende, J. Rush & S. Applegate

Your voice is warm and ten - der, a love that
But ne - ver won - der where I am 'cause I am

I could__ not for - sake.
al - ways__ by your side.
'Cause I am your la -

- dy__ and you are my man.__

When - ev - er you reach__ for me I'm gon - na do all that I can.__

Ev -en though there may be

We're head - ing for

some - thing, Some - where I've ne - ver been,____

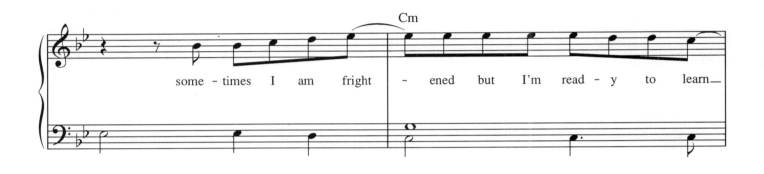

some - times I am fright - ened but I'm read - y to learn____

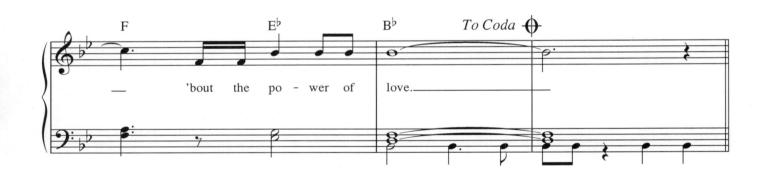

____ 'bout the po - wer of love.____

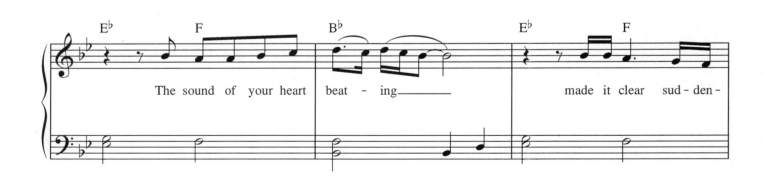

The sound of your heart beat - ing____ made it clear sud - den-

-ly. The feel-ing that I can't go___ on___

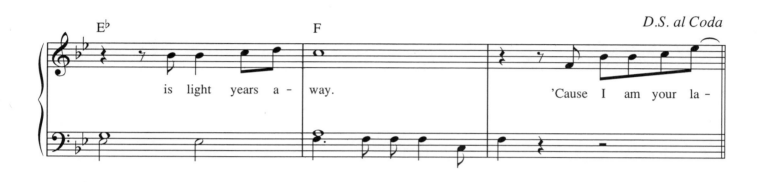

D.S. al Coda

is light years a-way. 'Cause I am your la-

CODA

The po-wer of love.___ The po-wer of love.___

The po-wer of love.___

I'm Your Angel

Words & Music by R. Kelly

Moderately slow

1. No moun-tain's too high for you to climb. All you
(Verse 2 see block lyric)

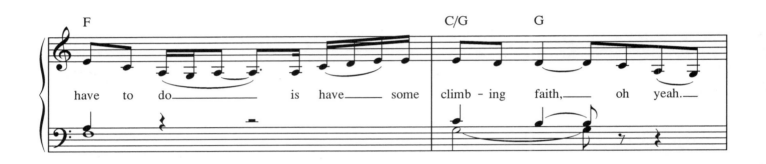

have to do is have some climb - ing faith, oh yeah.

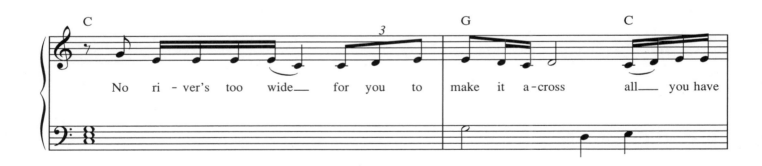

No ri - ver's too wide for you to make it a-cross all you have

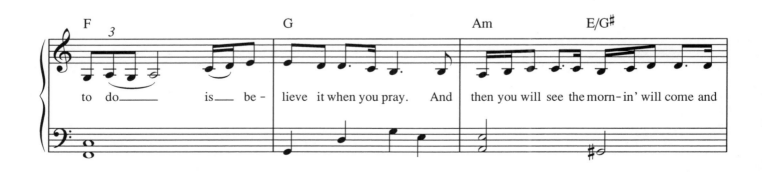

to do is be - lieve it when you pray. And then you will see the morn-in' will come and

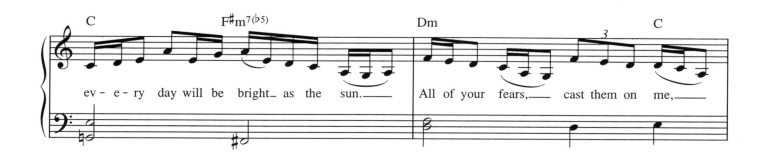

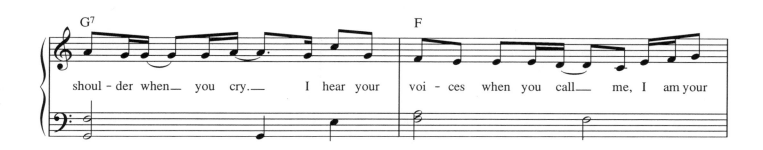

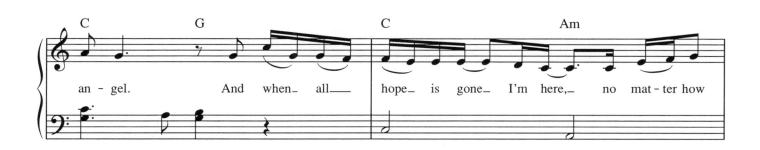

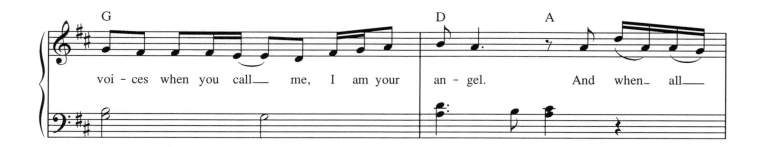

voi - ces when you call___ me, I am your an - gel. And when___ all___

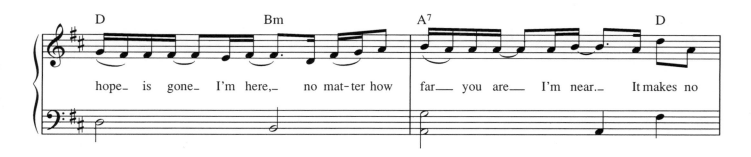

hope___ is gone___ I'm here,___ no mat-ter how far___ you are___ I'm near.___ It makes no

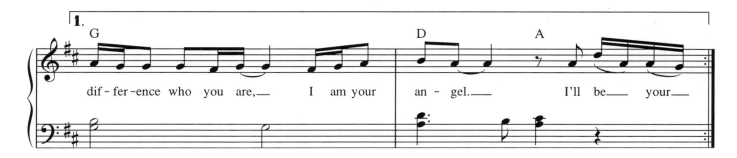

1.

dif - fer -ence who you are,___ I am your an - gel.___ I'll be___ your___

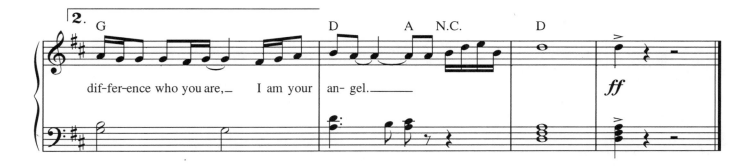

2.

dif-fer-ence who you are,___ I am your an- gel.___

Verse 2:

I saw your teardrops and I hear you crying
All you need is time, seek me and you shall find
You have everything you're still lonely
It don't have to be this way
Let me show you a better day
And then you will see the morning will come
And all of your days will be bright as the sun
So all of your fears, just cast them on me
How can I make you see?

I'll be your cloud *etc.*

Think Twice

Words & Music by Andy Hill & Pete Sinfield

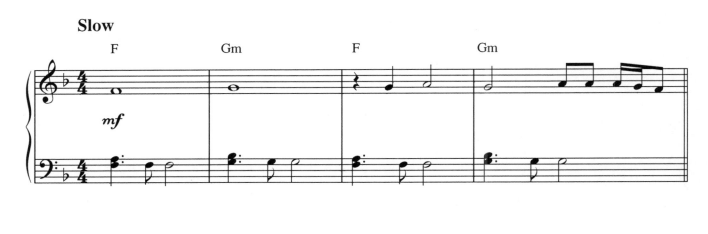

1. Don't think I can't feel that there's some - thing wrong,—
(Verse 2 see block lyric)

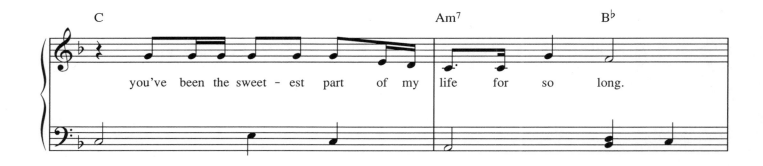

you've been the sweet - est part of my life for so long.

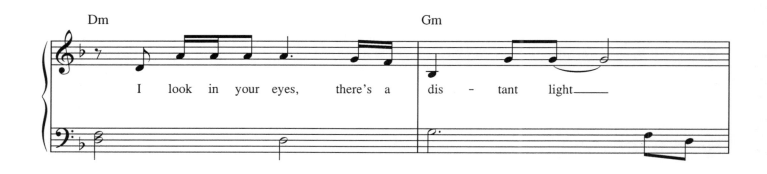

I look in your eyes, there's a dis - tant light———

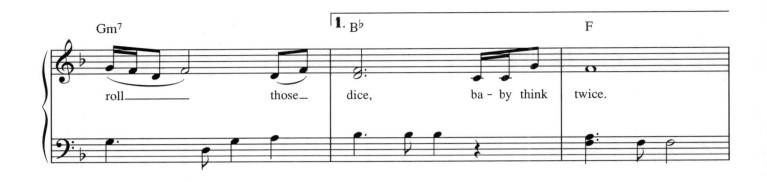

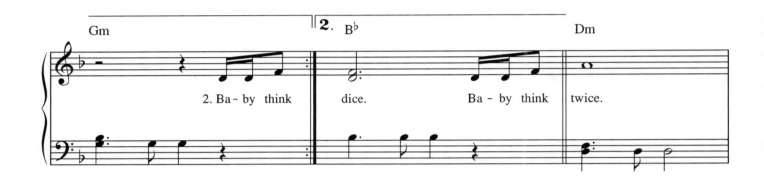

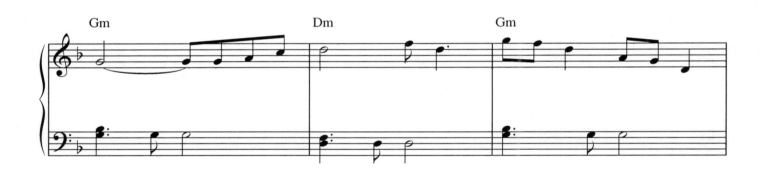

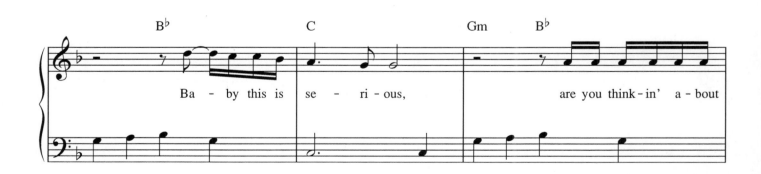

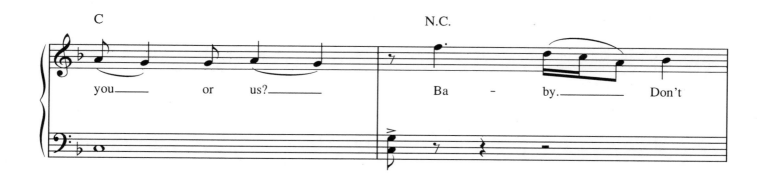

you____ or us?____ Ba - by.____ Don't

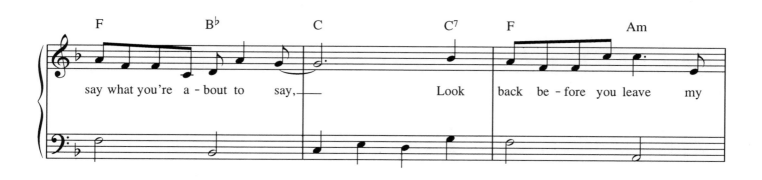

say what you're a-bout to say,__ Look back be-fore you leave my

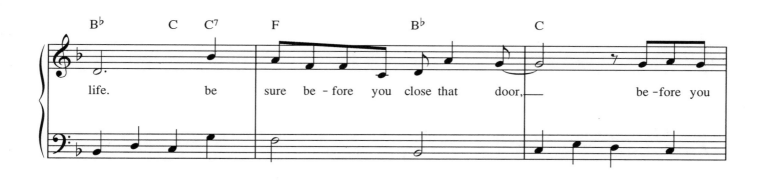

life. be sure be-fore you close that door,__ be-fore you

roll____ those_ dice. Don't say what you're a-bout to say,__

Look back be - fore you leave my life. be

sure be - fore you close that door,___ be - fore you roll___ those___

dice.___

Verse 2:

Baby think twice, for the sake of our love
For the memory,
For the fire and the faith
That was you and me.
Babe I know it ain't easy
When your soul cries out for the higher ground,
'Cause when you're halfway up
You're always halfway down.

But baby this is serious
Are you thinkin' 'bout you or us?